AN UNCONVENTIONAL MIND

Grace Roy

HOBART BOOKS

HOBART BOOKS

AN UNCONVENTIONAL MIND

First Published in 2023
by
Hobart Books, Oxfordshire, England

hobartbooks.com

Printed and bound in Great Britain.

An Unconventional Mind

By Grace Roy

To all of the amazing HCAs I
have met in my time.

A slightly unconventional book
for slightly unconventional minds.
Utilise this book in the way that you
can gain most from it, whether that be
(literally or figuratively)
tearing apart the nuggets of supposed
wisdom
and deriving your own morals from them
or plonking it beside your bed and
referring to it when you need a pick me up.
or a light stop-start book of nothings.

There is no structure to this wonky little
book, so...
Read front to back.
Read every other page.
Read the pages you feel drawn to.
Read one page and then regift to someone
whose brain appreciates the messy nature of
an unconventional brain encapsulated and
almost neatly arranged in one compact
article. Or perhaps if your situation is dire
enough, you find this book is best used in
lieu of toilet paper (pun unintended).

Read this when life seems particularly **dark
and twisty** or perhaps your brain feels
particularly **dark and twisty.**

An Ode To The Philosophers, Nihilists, Unconventional Thinkers, Those Who Feel a Little Lost & Anyone In Between.

Let this book be your comfort blanket.

The absence of a pufferfish

The absence of a pufferfish is never more apparent than when a pufferfish is not in your possession or in your line of sight. You never quite know when a pufferfish will be of use to you or in which way you may utilise it.

For example, when I set out on writing this book from an uncharacteristically comfy hospital bed, the company of a pufferfish soft toy would never have occurred to me as something which might settle the looming uncertainty that prolonged hospital stays tend to create.

But I have come to realise that Fyfe, my trusty pufferfish, most probably sitting beside me as you read this, is the little portion of comfort I didn't know I needed.

In short, sometimes you don't know what you need, until at the right moment, it crosses your path.

Live the full life of the mind,
exhilarated by new ideas,
intoxicated by the
romance of the unusual.

- Ernest Hemingway

Find joy in the mundane

The ability to experience genuine joy of the purest kind, solely from bearing witness to wearisome human activity, is a skill to hold on to and make use of when you feel you've come to a standstill and life itself has become momentarily wearisome. However, make sure to never become complacent with joy found in the mundane alone. Becoming accustomed to your only dopamine hits being derived from the drab aspects of life allows you to linger in ignorance. Ignorant to the all-consuming, breathtaking moments of joy that await you.

Completing your daily dishwashing accompanied by 'Whitney Houston's Feel-Good Hits'.
[Joy in the mundane]

Racing along the pier, following a wholesome day in the sun with the friends that make you laugh until your body aches and your pores leak euphoria. Hoping to obtain a doughnut or two, to devour as you watch the sunset.

[pure, all-consuming joy]

Home

Home, supposedly, is where one hangs one's hat...

...if you are anything like me, I have never once 'hung' my hat anywhere, rather discarded it in some cupboard and not looked its way until the next commencement of a cold winter.

So, humour me when I say:

I think home is the thing that you long for most, over anything else, in its absence. Whether that be a person, a period of your life, an ensemble of your favourite beings, a field conveniently located miles from civilisation, an entire country, or conventional brick and mortar.

Home is where you draw the most comfort from.

Pick your grudges

Some people, by nature are champion grudge holders.
Some people forgive and forget, almost to a fault.
Some have no moral conscience whatsoever and couldn't begin to verbalise the nature of their grudge if they did have a grudge against someone or something.

Some are under the age of three and couldn't even pronounce 'grudge'.

Holding a grudge can be useful in a multitude of situations.
Finally, bearing a grudge over a situation that another has put you in, (as opposed to letting it go) might enable it to re-occur, thus creating necessary boundaries. Sometimes boundaries are a finite detail we dismiss, when in fact they might just be the key to maintaining what sanity we retain. Equally, 'boundaries' can be an eye-roll term along with 'mindfulness' and the likes. Regardless of your degree of cynicism about the concept of boundary setting, it still stands that holding a grudge is often a healthy decision.

On the flip side we can find ourselves beginning to close up. Encasing ourselves in

the long list of grudges we have fought to keep in our grasp, some warranted, some not.
The ones that aren't so justifiable, we cling to either out of fear of being hurt again or because we have had them in a tight hold for such a long time that we have forgotten why they were important to us. That isn't to say there is no good reason to still dwell on a grudge, which is why I would suggest to 'pick your grudges'. Just as it is taught that you should pick 'your battles', picking what to let go of in accordance with your intuition can be uncomfortable, yet so freeing. Letting go doesn't have to mean rekindling relationships or reconciling with people who are no longer relevant to us. People don't even need to be made aware that you no longer hold a grudge – just having that knowledge to yourself simply allows past events, actions and words to become irrelevant to you. A reduction of metaphorical bric-a-brac cluttering your brain if you will. No forgiveness needs to take place, instead just letting go.

However, I would have to argue that *some* grudges are 100% valid. Mainly in regard to siblings, because I personally, am not letting go of that incident with the vodka, so cruelly taken from me on my 17th birthday.

Where that occurrence takes up capacity in my head, I have learned to let go of other occurrences nearly equally as mortifying as stolen vodka at the age of 17...
Pick your grudges.

<u>Authenticity</u>

I would advise against kicking yourself. It seems a very counterproductive practice.

However, if you let another individual's opinion dictate your life choices you *will* kick yourself when you come to realise none of the choices you made were authentically yours.

Ice cream

There is never a good reason to decline an ice cream from an ice cream van.

Unless you are lactose intolerant.

uNCoNvenTiOnaL

Being a landlord to an unconventional brain
is both rewarding and challenging; the cogs
that are said to turn in one's head may not
be made from carbon-steel alloys but
something more along the lines of jelly,
which never fails to forge a <u>beautifully</u>
<u>disastrous outcome.</u>
Such a uniquely wired mind looks somewhat
similar to the underneath of a sofa, an
eclectic mix of treasures, none of which
relate to one another. Essentially it is a
blessing to have a brain that is so wildly
unlike any other; from such minds, the most
astounding things in existence are born,
endless talent and limitless creativity
breathed into the atmosphere. You and your
unconventional brain have the might to
impact the world in such a distinctive and
enchanting way.
Each mind has its own format,
and no two look the same in structure. Some
minds have infinite filing cabinets, some just
have a few stray intellectual-sounding words
to recycle, drifting around their brain. Some
have vast seas of knowledge, pickpocketed
from every corner of the world, some have a
typewriter consistently narrating their

thoughts, no typist to be seen. Some have regimented thoughts, marching like a parade meticulously covering all grounds of the brain. Some have a board of critics who file away only the best of the best thoughts, thoughts that might one day make it big. The life of such thoughts begins in luxury diamond-encrusted filing cabinets being primed to venture beyond the cerebrum to be deposited via the oral region, then existing in auditory format for the masses to hear and applaud and love and live by and eventually preach to a second generation.

I imagine a brain requires its own shelving system, but the mental shelves of someone like you and me seem to have collapsed in a hurricane of messy contemplation, leaving behind a literary rubble of nonsense and non-nonsense: (sense)

On the next page is a visual display of an unconventional brain.
Not my unconventional brain,
but an unconventional brain, nevertheless.

I'm going to keep on the run
I'm going to have me some fun
If it costs me my very last dime
If I wind up broke oh well
I'll always remember that I had a swinging time
I'm gonna give it everything I've got
Lady luck please let the dice stay hot
Let me shoot a seven with every shot
Viva Las Vegas, Viva Las Vegas
Viva Las Vegas

ISBN: 978-1-914322-06-8

brass swivel for glass blowing

Farrokh Bulsara

stickyyy

rabid teabags

needlessly

endless

cardiovascular themed weddings

astragal

needles

jellied eels antys, dévintys tvidą

astrovan 1985 the smell of numbers

vignette filters arbitrary ghosts

K 389 W. 1830 South

Ste. 700 horizontal % quashed ☀
          hyperboles

yosemite bowline

Salt Lake City, UT 84115 URGENCY

(801) 487-1300 southern comfort

discarded motels

reminder for philip: halloween in three days

socialists eating jackfruit broth pittenweem

socrates profundities liquidity

twelvethousandeighthundredandfiftyfour

Whilst still on the topic of convention or lack thereof...

Here is a space to splatter your 'unconvention'.
Do with it what you want but don't you dare stay inside the lines. Because living within the confines of neatly packed boxes is... well... conventional.

Feeling **blue**?

bluebirds
blueberries.
blue light.
rhythm and **blues**.
blueprints.
blue to the power of **blue** to the power of
blue
= **blue** cubed.
blue whales.
Monday **blues.**
black and **blue.**
blue suede shoes.

when you surround yourself entirely in something, you let it suffocate you until slowly it encapsulates you. It becomes you.

And the only way to become a**blue**nt of it completely is to remove yourself from it. Not just intend to remove yourself eventually, not talk about the notion 'til you're **blue** in the face, but to be proactive and really remove yourself. Run from it until you're out of the **blue**...

...because the grass is always greener

Breakage

Give yourself full permission to
take a break.
Breathe,
then continue.
Without such permission you will
inevitably
B R E A K
not just crack,
but shatter,
shatter into pieces that can be haphazardly
glued back together,
however, after a long session filled with glue-
sticks and attempted amendment,
most likely you will no longer be the same as
you were before.

Intense breakage.

"Sometimes the kindest thing you can do for someone is to stop giving them your kindness, because what you are teaching them by your unconditional kindness is 'You can treat me like a piece of garbage and I'm still gonna be overly kind to you'."
-Najwa Zebian

A List of Lists

Achievements list

There is every chance that you already have a to-do list that looms over you. In many respects a to-do list is great motivation to get up and do! But all too often we find ourselves agonising over such lists and feeling like an inadequate husband, wife, parent, child, employee and overall human if we are unable to achieve every last thing on the list with full efficiency.

Make note, daily, of one thing you have achieved, anything ranging from managing to brush your teeth to having completed reading every book written by Mary Shelley, or maybe you rescued an overturned ladybird and made someone laugh all in the space of an hour. Maybe all you did today was open this book, at this page. No matter what, you will always have achieved *something.*

After a while you will have a small collection of achievements to look over. Instead of reflecting on your day or week and beating yourself up over your lack of productivity, you can refer to your list and see that you did, in fact, achieve lots!

Brain splat list

Give your brain a spring clean. Put some chilled music on or a bit of death metal (no judgement here) and just brain dump. Your weirdest thoughts, your scariest thoughts, those reoccurring thoughts that you are so bored of constantly shutting down. Record them all until you have a substantial list of things that are holding you back. Thoughts that no longer need to take up brain capacity... let them out on paper, and whilst they are there in front of you, you can delve into the patterns that you begin to see or the stressors that birth these thoughts. You can gain so much insight in seeing your trickiest thoughts neatly compiled in a list. If a deep psychological dive isn't what you need right now, you still have decluttered your brain, even if only slightly.

Comforts

Being knowledgeable on what most comforts you is a necessity to make it through life. Make individual lists of the books, the films, the songs and the memories that provide optimal comfort. This way, when you are faced with unavoidable unpleasantries, or mild inconveniences, you have a compilation of all the things that feel safe and familiar to you. Having a general list of comforts or specific individual lists on standby provides

somewhere to turn to when your brain won't quieten or you feel particularly on edge, cutting out the middleman. The middleman in this case being a little man running round your brain on a frantic mission to try and find order
and safety
and comfort
and in doing so creating more mess, knocking over furniture, and spilling mini coffee cups of comfort onto the floor. Middleman can now be eradicated, and you are promptly reminded by your handy list that an episode or two of Scooby Doo will bring immediate calm to your panicked brain.

Gratitude list
It's often hard to be grateful when *she* has this, and *he* has that. The difference between want and jealously can easily become distorted.
They have the job you want.
They have the family dynamic you want.
They have the house you want.
They have the figure you want.
They have that oddly specific kettle you were after before it sold out.
They seem to have it all.
So let me ask you this:
If you were suddenly rushed into hospital and were set to stay there longer than you'd

like, the only material possessions with you are quite literally *material* possessions... your clothes.
Your hoodie, shorts, underwear, and crocs. No familiar faces, just standoffish doctors and a glacially cold, clinical-smelling, curtain-walled room with an exceptionally lumpy bed for you to begin pondering your ill health in. All the while, putting up with a leak that keeps periodically wetting your socks through the holes in your crocs.
What would you be grateful for?

In such an unpleasant situation who or what would you be most grateful for?

A comfy bed? Your family's presence? Good health? Your second-rate kettle?

All starters for your gratitude list, because no matter what situation you find yourself in, you still have *something*. It might not be a lot and it might not be what *they* have, but you have something.
Of course, when you feel that life isn't giving you what you what you think you need, being frustrated and upset are very valid feelings. But at least you have your 'somethings'.
Having a physical list of things that you are grateful for has been suggested by research

as an action that improves overall
happiness.

Ice cream flavours
Unless you aspire to be an ice cream
connoisseur, or you can analyse a selection
of varying ice creams and derive some deep
philosophical meaning from its flavour, this
list has no practical benefits besides pure
entertainment.
Make a list of all the flavours, wacky or
regular, that should be available in ice cream
form, all the things that Ben & Jerry's are
yet to get creative enough to produce, like:
Carrot cake,
Gummy Bear
Lasagne?
Caviar and dragonfruit

Go wild.

A list of lists to make in the future

Making lists to occupy one's mind is a task that requires no great effort and allows you to take a minute to collect yourself, so here are a few list suggestions:

Baby name lists,

Worst films you've seen,

Favourite songs,

Ill-fitting pet names,

Tried and tested recipes,

Beautiful lyrics,

Questions that appear to have no answer,

Funniest memories,

Countries to visit,

What you think each celebrity's death row meal would be,

Favourite childhood TV shows,

Best dad jokes,

Movies that should've been award-winning,

Foods that just SHOULD NOT exist,

Controversial opinions,

Essentials you'd take to a desert island,

Things you are proud of,

Morning and evening routine essentials,

The states of America you'd like to visit and in what order

...to name a few.

Karaoke

If you want to get up and sing on a karaoke night, get up and sing.

Uncertainty

When your life becomes riddled with uncertainty and your brain starts to function lopsidedly, you can always rely on

11:59 pm

11:59 pm is the one thing you can fall back on repeatedly; it passes every day without fail; it turns up on time every day, no tardiness. Eventually you will come to appreciate the consistency of 11:59 pm amidst the chaos and uncertainty of society. When the time finally does roll round, you have one minute remaining, one minute to reflect, cry, scream about your day and then 'just like clockwork' your day has come to an end, and you can restart in any way you see fit.

Be comfortable with the passing of each day and feel blessed that you have another day ahead of you. And know that you have the ability to make this day significantly better than the last.

Your best

You did the best you could with what was
available to you at the time, don't beat
yourself up over your past self, past
decisions, past limitations. You did the
best you could.

Useful – or not so useful – tips, that might one day come in handy

1. **Marshmallows**

   If you are someone who frequents campfires (or even if you have never once attended a campfire) then it may be useful to know that the optimal distance between burning coal and your marshmallow, to achieve a *toasted,* rather than burnt, marshmallow is **six inches**. (Which, for reference is roughly the length of a toothbrush.)

2. **Tin foil**

   When you lack wrapping paper, tin foil is an ideal substitute... It's cost-effective and makes for a highly 'reflective' gift. (Although there is always the option, when you find yourself in dire need of wrapping paper, of going to the shop and purchasing brand new wrapping paper.)

3. **Chinchillas**

   Should you ever find yourself the temporary guardian of a chinchilla, then you should be aware that it is essential for these creatures to be kept in dry, well-ventilated rooms, at temperatures ranging from 10° to 18° C, to prevent illness. They must also be kept away from the interference of draughts or other pets.

4. Lobster allergies

If you are allergic to lobsters, my recommendation would be to give lobsters a wide berth. Equally if you find yourself in a position where giving lobsters a wide berth is unachievable, my recommendation would be to make yourself familiar with Loratadine (brand name: Claritin), so long as you are not also allergic to it *and* lobsters. Although it may come as a surprise to you, seeking immediate advice from someone with current medical qualifications may, in fact, be your best bet.

5. Bumps in the night

If you begin to hear creaks and bumps around your house in the dead of night then it's probably your cat deliberately stepping on the creaky floorboard whilst on its prowl, just to keep you immobile and scared under a blanket. If you find yourself hearing these same noises in the absence of a pet cat, make even louder, weirder noises in response, unleash your primal instincts, assert your dominance, and scare off whatever demon or rusty boiler is creating such scary noises.

6. Grandma's refrigerator

When your fridge becomes unbearably full, which mostly tends to happen around Christmastime, why not locate a relative who lives alone and therefore presumably has more fridge space than you do? Then, with or without their consent, use their spare fridge space as your own, depending on the whereabouts* of this relative and their spacious fridge.

*Because what use is your grandma and her fridge to you, if she lives in Slovenia whilst you live in Surrey?

7. Cake cutting

Use (preferably unused) dental floss to cut perfect slices in a cake.

Clarifying shampoo

If you are familiar with clarifying shampoo and the purpose it serves, then you will be well aware that it works in removing colour from hair.

Don't let clarifying *people* into your life to strip you of *your* colour.

"Slow down you're doing fine, you can't be everything you wanna be before your time".
-**Vienna by Billy Joel**

Rainy Monday Evening

Sometimes you have to let a rainy Monday
evening be a rainy Monday evening.
Not plaster it in makeup or drown it in vodka
shots.
In the words of a legendary band:
'Let It Be'.

Unbearable vs uncomfortable

On many occasions throughout the day (or you take all of this out and say 'often') I find myself uttering these words: 'unbearable or uncomfortable?' and often my decisions, big or small, hinge on the answer.

Life is accompanied by many accidental unpleasantries; accidental because by design they are not awful things even if, to some individuals, they are *beyond* awful.

My go-to example of this is the milk round that I had the misfortune of doing for a brief period at the age of fifteen, with shifts that commenced at 11 pm and sometimes dragged on until 4 am. A five-hour shift might seem like nothing to some, for example healthcare staff who work twelve hours or doctors on call or any number of jobs that require less than convenient hours.

But this is where subjectivity comes into play. I, as an already exhausted fifteen-year-old girl, fresh out of exam season, *despised* my duty of running around with heavy crates of milk in the dead of night with a man I barely knew. To some people that job description sounds like a walk in the park and that is fine: subjectivity.

In this short period of my life where I felt stuck in a situation that filled me with pure dread and caused many anxiety-infused, restless nights, I developed the 'unbearable or uncomfortable' mindset.

Life will inevitably throw unbearable situations at you, ones that are beyond your control, the type that have you questioning everything and could quite easily tip you into an existential crisis. But some unbearable situations, such as a dreadful milk round, can be a quick fix. Quit the job. Leave the boyfriend. Find a different place to live. All things that, admittedly, don't sound like 'quick fixes', and I understand that they are all things 'easier said than done'. However, in the grand scheme of life, leaving the job, girlfriend, boyfriend, flat and whatever else may be causing you copious amounts of stress, are all decisions that your future self will not regret one bit.

You were not put on this planet to live a life full of unbearable situations that gradually tear you down, until either (as already mentioned in this book) you are subject to intense breakage, or you become accustomed to your life feeling like a cycle of insufferable chores. We get one shot at life, and I am a firm believer that it is there to be lived to its absolute fullest. Fill your days with belly laughing, and backpacking Europe, and dancing with strangers, gone midnight. Seek out your soulmate and hidden waterfalls. Get wine drunk with your best friend, gatecrash a stag night (an activity my dearest mother partook in). Eat noodles with chopsticks in China, go sledding when Britain offers more than a pathetic icing sugar-sprinkle of snow. Try every flavour of slushies that you can find, keep going to that festival you love beyond your 60s. Find music that makes your heart happy, have a child.

Live. Your. Life.

Avoid ALL unnecessary unbearable situations because life is meant to be so much more than bearable, it's meant to be beautiful and breathtaking. You are supposed to end life with an infinite stash of memories, stories that you cherish and retell to kids, grandkids or anyone who will listen.

That aside, it would be exceptionally ignorant of me to not acknowledge that sometimes situations arise that aren't ideal, in which you'd rather not be at a certain place, doing a certain thing, at a certain time. If those certain things are necessary stepping stones in getting to where you want to be in life, then evaluate. Ask yourself, 'Is this unbearable or merely uncomfortable?'.

If the latter, then grin and bear it until it's over, until it has provided a gateway to leading the life you desire to lead.

If it is, in fact, unbearable, pack it in, find another way to achieve your goals that

doesn't cost you your sanity, will to live or...
anything. Find a way that has no adverse
effects on you and your life. Use this same
question even in making smaller, less
significant decisions.

Is it *uncomfortable* to sit through a lecture on
why Ludwig Wittgenstein was a crucial figure
in pioneering analytical philosophy or is it
actually unbearable?

Is it unbearable to walk to the shop for milk
in the pouring rain or simply uncomfortable?
Your call.

Quelle vie enchanteresse.

Milyen varázslatos élet.

Ce viata incantatoare.

nə sehrli həyatdır.

τι μαγευτική ζωή.

Ze bizimodu liluragarria.

Waa maxay nolosha soo jiidashada leh.

多麼迷人的生活.

He oranga whakamiharo.

किं मनोहरं जीवनम्

Que vida encantadora.

ինչ դյութիչ կյանք է

wat een betoverend leven.

nga bulamu bwa kuloga

ямар сэтгэл татам амьдрал вэ

thật là một cuộc sống mê hoặc

wat en verzauberend Liewen

ni maisha ya uchawi gani

anong kaakit-akit na buhay

ช่างเป็นชีวิตที่น่าหลงใหล

qanday maftunkor hayot

cóż za czarujące życie

какая очаровательная жизнь

Liema ħajja enchanting

am fywyd hudolus

mikä lumoava elämä

What an enchanting life.

Morals and sweetcorn

Establish your morals. Know what is fundamentally important to you. But *do not* spend a lifetime searching for your own personal philosophy. It will all come naturally; it will prevail on its own and it will shine through in your personality and actions.

Your own moral value and personal philosophy does not have to be profound and impressive. Pretending that something is of great importance to you in order to appeal to a set group of people, or to create the façade that you are articulate and woke and vegan and that you are politically knowledgeable, will expend too much of your energy.

If your personal philosophy consists of:

'Lying is always wrong' and **'Sweetcorn is massively overlooked and deserves more attention in the media'**...

that is fine, no need to dress it up.

What is important to you, is important to you.

You are capable,
you are worthy,
you are deserving,
you are loved,
you are allowed to heal,
you are allowed to live freely,
you are needed on this planet.

You are needed. Let that sink in.

Always pay attention to the cheesy
motivational quotes that are plastered on
mugs and decorative pillows.
        Sometimes they hold truth.

Live, laugh, be calm.

Becoming who you are at your core

It's natural to be afraid of taking the steps that you need to take in order to align your external presentation with your soul, but don't let fear be the thing that prevents the creation of a magnificent being.

Exist.
And enjoy your existence,
learn to see it as blessing.
And exist to the fullest extent.
And exist more than you knew possible.
Exist.

Heirloom Recipes

Over the years I have come across a great many people whose families have a cherished, almost always secret, family recipe. Written out in calligraphy on yellowing, flour-coated paper, or jotted on the back of an electricity bill. Either way, such a recipe is sure to have remained nearly entirely the same as when it was first created, decades, if not centuries, ago. A few amendments and personal touches added on occasion, but at heart it remains the same adored family recipe.

An 'heirloom recipe'.

Heirloom recipes hold a special type of comfort. Fondly reminiscing on the times your great-grandad, grandma, grandad, dad, mum, cousin affectionately made you that family-specific vindaloo, speaks to the age-old notion that food is internationally the language of love.

I knew an Italian family once upon a time
who in my eyes held the key
to happiness in the form of a secret pizza
base recipe.
There is something so, so magical about
that, about a recipe and the evolution of a
recipe. Ingredients known by few, the
combination of said ingredients shared with
and loved by hundreds if not thousands.
If you happen *not* to have an heirloom-type
recipe, then forge your own. Take an already
established recipe and add measures of
cardamom or cinnamon, salt, cranberries,
nutritional yeast or garlic, hoisin duck, white
chocolate or Worcestershire sauce, caramel
or oregano, whatever takes your fancy.
Taste test,
add ingredients,
subtract ingredients,
taste test,
Repeat, then pass down for generations.

My 'heirloom recipe'

(Side note: This recipe, I am afraid to say, *is not* an exotic mix of top-secret ingredients, hence my decision to share with whomever bothers to read this book. If you are seeking something **AWE-INSPIRING**, something so **SOPHISTICATED** that your palate itself begins to question whether such **BOLD** and **BRILLIANT** flavours have graced its presence before... this is not the recipe for you. If your tastebuds need a **THRILL**, more than can be offered by a mere woman of north-west England, who is pleased by a simple freezer meal, try Fesenjan Chicken, a **SOUL-WARMING** Iranian dish, brimming with the **RICH** flavour combination of pomegranate molasses and walnuts. If that won't do I could offer a near endless list of **IMPRESSIVE**-sounding desserts, the type that royalty might be familiar with. Desserts fit for a king; Sheep milk mousse with pandan curd and puffed rice or aerated elderflower parfait alongside Sablé Breton or Kashata with a side of blow-torched berries. Although personally, if I ever found myself dining with princes and princesses, queens and kings, I'd be sure to introduce them to Aldi's biscuit selection, the commoners' equivalent of **MICHELIN STAR-WORTHY** desserts.

If you happen to be of Irish descent or have a penchant for bread, then you are most likely aware of the existence of soda bread and soda farls, which came into existence in 1845 during the Irish famine. Easy to make, with ingredients accessible to all, it was perfect for mopping up a stew or as a standalone soul warmer. The perfect stodge food, rainy day food, 'I feel unwell' food, 'I miss the smell of my mum's cooking' food. Comfort food for the occasions when you seek comfort via food – food therapy, almost.

Quick and easy to make (although I may be biased), this bread is just all-round brilliant. Then again bread is very rarely not brilliant.

Ingredients

300g plain flour
½ tsp of salt
Heaped tsp of baking soda
225ml of milk
1½ tsp of lemon juice
And a pinch of sugar

Soda farls

1. Mix together all your dry ingredients, sparing a little bit of flour. Create a 'well' in the resulting mix within the bowl.

2. Combine and briefly mix the lemon juice and milk before pouring it into the previously created 'well'. By hand, swiftly work the milk into the rest of the ingredients to form a dough.

3. Preheat a skillet on a medium to medium-high temperature.

4. Once all ingredients are fully combined, knead on a lightly floured surface and roll out until the dough is just over an inch thick.

5. Score the dough twice down the middle, creating 4 equal quadrants and transfer to the skillet or pan with a small amount of flour to prevent sticking.

6. Cook for 10 minutes before flipping and cooking the other side for a further 10 minutes or until golden brown and visibly risen.

7. Then locate the butter and three companions willing to taste test your butter smothered heaven-in-bread-form. Alternatively, you could locate the butter, smother your masterpiece in it and devour all four pieces freshly cooked in one sitting! Either way, enjoy your stodge and I will live in hope that at least one other person can find some sort of deep comfort from this recipe, just as my ancestors and I have done.

Four things I would consider essential for survival

(Human survival, of course; to my knowledge this does not apply to crustaceans.)

F.R.O.F
Who doesn't love a good old Americanised acronym.

.Food
.Relationships
.Oxygen
.Fluids

So, eat well,
love intensely – both platonically and romantically,
breathe (you fortunately don't have much choice with this one)
and drink (take that instruction however you see fit, not that I endorse substituting water for wine)

Bask in a familiar misery for the rest of your life or make the decision to tirelessly hunt for that unfamiliar joy that *does* exist (albeit, well hidden amongst a society sadly accustomed to, and complacent with, their misery)

That is the most radical action you can take.

M E R A K I
[may-rah-kee]
Greek

[adj.] when you do something with soul, passion, creativity, and the purest form of love: putting a piece of yourself into what you do.

Let your hair down

Let your hair down once in a while, let it
blow in the wind.
If you happen to be bald and bearded, let
your beard down and feel free... let your
beard blow in the wind...
If none of these conditions apply to you then
nor does this hippie, yoga-esque advice.

10 types of people to trust

(I am in no way, endorsing having trust in just anyone and everyone, that being the easiest way to get hurt. However, these 5 types of people are a great start if you, rightly, find difficulty having confidence in humanity. All the information below has been collected as result of personal experience but allow your instincts to intervene when it comes to choosing who to trust.)

1. An individual who *always* has a book on their person.

2. An individual who is willing to lend you a fully functioning electric heater.

3. Individuals who feed ducks with duck-feed rather than bread (they tend to have no ulterior motive when interacting with you. If they are conscientious enough to feed a duck, taking into account its intended diet rather than a human food which, in fact, can lead to it becoming greatly malnourished, then you can more than likely trust them to make you a brew without the addition of cyanide.)

4. Health care professionals who go by a shortened version of their name (e.g. Charlotte or Elizabeth or Jessica who

introduce themselves as Charlie, Beth and Jess.

5. People whose childhood teddy happened to be a rabbit.

6. That small percentage of humanity who halt alongside you when your shoelaces choose defiance and (ever so inconveniently) untie themselves, rather than continuing and leaving you and your wayward shoelaces behind.

7. An extension of the previous bullet point, that even more minuscule number of humans who, not only pause their journey on account of your shoelaces, but additionally tie said laces for you. (Most likely doing so after observing your incompetence in the field of lace tying.)

8. People who can no longer hack a Sambuca shot and will openly admit that they can no longer hack a Sambuca shot.

9. Those who unapologetically create unorthodox and loud, messy art forms

(be they literature, music, paintings, or
contemporary dance routines)

10. People who are not afraid to eat
'teatime foods' for breakfast.

Unshakeable colds

An 'unshakeable cold', no matter how long-lived, is never truly unshakeable. You will not live out the rest of your life with an insistent cough and runny nose. The same is applicable to those dark times in life; that darkness will not be your lifetime's companion It will pass, in the meantime treat yourself tenderly, the way you would treat a loved one if they had a cold.

Two things to have in order before you die:

1. Your will
2. Having smile lines etched deep into your cheeks and a heart fully enriched with experience and love, a soul that achieved its full potential, and eyes that have seen the world, and read books, and observed the night sky and its splatter of silvery stars, and a brain that pondered the universe and remained curious, always seeking an answer.

Most amusing paint shade names

A trait I have no shame in having carried from childhood through to adolescence is having an intense fascination in shades of paint and the amusing names given to them. I adapted the strange yet harmless pastime of taking a trip to hardware stores and focused on my mission of hunting down the paint section just to giggle at some of the allocated paint names. So, when boredom or anxiety (or both) simultaneously begin to infiltrate your brain, refer to a trusty paint catalogue and explore the most outlandish, comical and downright ludicrous names.

A few personal favourites:

·Overtly Olive

·**Blue**berry White – comical for obvious reasons.

·*Deep Aubergine* – 'Honey, deep aubergine would make a great feature wall in the lounge'.

·Almost Oyster – I would love to see exactly what an *almost* oyster looks like.

·Potentially Purple – so I'm looking at a 50% chance of actually receiving *purple* paint?

·Grandma's Refrigerator

·Mayonnaise

·Baby toes

·Not enough chocolate syrup mom – above all else, the lack of punctuation is laughable.
·Cantankerous Coyote – this one I am sure was someone's attempt at impressing their boss with their vast and varying vocabulary.
·Sweet potato Surprise
·Thimble Case
.Mole's Breath
.Dead Salmon
.Elephant's Whisper

Use this space to add your own stupidly marvellous paint name suggestions, the types that would get you either hired or fired at Dulux:

·

·

·

·

Appreciate the moments of beauty that may cross your path; never overlook them because you are in such eager pursuit of your dreams.

General life advice

You may not be where you need to be in life, but you are exactly where you are meant to be.

Don't rush yourself. Do everything you need to do at leisure; enjoy the journey.

Allow yourself to properly rest, between meeting goals.

Appreciate the moments of beauty that may cross your path, never overlook them because you are in such eager pursuit of your dreams.

Be realistic and 'overly' ambitious simultaneously.

Listen to others and be open to taking on board their opinion, but ultimately don't let the judgement of others stop you from doing **anything**; this is your life to lead.

Trust your gut; it's a built-in gift from the gods.

Life is far too short to stress the small things.

Never trust claw machines.

Some individuals, by nature, are less compassionate than a foldable camping chair.

Interesting words that will expand your vocabulary and give you an enormous sense of intellectuality.

(Hidden in a word search to soothe your mind or tame your raging restlessness.)

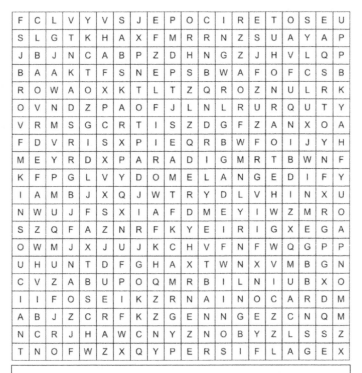

F	C	L	V	Y	V	S	J	E	P	O	C	I	R	E	T	O	S	E	U
S	L	G	T	K	H	A	X	F	M	R	R	N	Z	S	U	A	Y	A	P
J	B	J	N	C	A	B	P	Z	D	H	N	G	Z	J	H	V	L	Q	P
B	A	A	K	T	F	S	N	E	P	S	B	W	A	F	O	F	C	S	B
R	O	W	A	O	X	K	T	L	T	Z	Q	R	O	Z	N	U	L	R	K
O	V	N	D	Z	P	A	O	F	J	L	N	L	R	U	R	Q	U	T	Y
V	R	M	S	G	C	R	T	I	S	Z	D	G	F	Z	A	N	X	O	A
F	D	V	R	I	S	X	P	I	E	Q	R	B	W	F	O	I	J	Y	H
M	E	Y	R	D	X	P	A	R	A	D	I	G	M	R	T	B	W	N	F
K	F	P	G	L	V	Y	D	O	M	E	L	A	N	G	E	D	I	F	Y
I	A	M	B	J	X	Q	J	W	T	R	Y	D	L	V	H	I	N	X	U
N	W	U	J	F	S	X	I	A	F	D	M	E	Y	I	W	Z	M	R	O
S	Z	Q	F	A	Z	N	R	F	K	Y	E	I	R	I	G	X	E	G	A
O	W	M	J	X	J	U	J	K	C	H	V	F	N	F	W	Q	G	P	P
U	H	U	N	T	D	F	G	H	A	X	T	W	N	X	V	M	B	G	N
C	V	Z	A	B	U	P	O	Q	M	R	B	I	L	N	I	U	B	X	O
I	I	F	O	S	E	I	K	Z	R	N	A	I	N	O	C	A	R	D	M
A	B	J	Z	C	R	F	K	Z	G	E	N	N	G	E	Z	C	N	Q	M
N	C	R	J	H	A	W	C	N	Y	Z	N	O	B	Y	Z	L	S	S	Z
T	N	O	F	W	Z	X	Q	Y	P	E	R	S	I	F	L	A	G	E	X

Apricate, Draconian, Edify, Esoteric, Insouciant, Melange, Obdurate, Paradigm, Persiflage, Zenith

Oxford Dictionary definitions
(Because, what use is a word destitute of its meaning?)

apricate [verb]
To bask in the sun.
draconian [adj]
(Of laws or their application) excessively harsh and severe.
edify [verb]
Instruct or improve (someone) morally or intellectually.
esoteric [adj]
Intended for or likely to be understood by only a small number of people with a specialised knowledge or interest.
insouciant [adj]
Showing a casual lack of concern.
melange [noun]
A varied mixture.
obdurate [adj]
Stubbornly refusing to change one's opinion or course of action.
paradigm [noun]
A typical example or pattern of something; a pattern or model.
persiflage [noun]
Light and slightly contemptuous mockery or banter.
zenith [noun]
The time at which something is most powerful or successful.

Reinvention

Keep it in the forefront of your mind that you can always reinvent yourself, with any degree of health, any financial position, any living situation, any age and with any inch of the fear of judgement being harboured within you, you **can** reinvent yourself, you can start afresh.

That's not to say do not be content with who you are, but if your life is not as fulfilling as it has the potential to be, then make a change. If life has gotten ever so slightly boring, make a change.

Reinvent yourself over and over.
You only live once.

Living, breathing, functioning

Being a living, breathing, functioning human leaves you susceptible to a great many things...

...meningitis, diabetes, cystic echinococcosis, heart break, homicide, motorcycle crashes, splinters, nosy neighbours, theft, awkward interactions with cashiers that replay in your head for several years following such...

Subsequently it is easy to lose sight of the fact that being a living, breathing, functioning human leaves you susceptible to many great things...

...parenthood, the fusion of two effortlessly compatible souls, ventures to exotic destinations (Fiji, Easter Island, Dubrovnik... Cheltenham?), hearing beautiful melodies, the ability to make another laugh and the attached contentment, river jumping in mid-July, dog ownership, feeling the heat of a roaring bonfire on frosty, otherwise inhospitable days...

It's about swallowing THAT pill: *Lifecanbeshitfromtimetotimeazine,* along with your multivitamins and other necessary medication.

Acknowledging that you are not immune to life's shortcomings and misfortune but <u>knowing</u> that existence also prescribes many joys, no matter how small a dose.

Ceilings and fridges (grandmas' fridges in particular)

It is useful to have a space that sums you
up, whether it be your
ceiling
or your plain white bedroom wall
or your fridge
or a collection of *messy* art
or a collection of *organised* art
or your personal array of literature.
Create a space that upon your closest
acquaintance's viewing, they are compelled
to say. 'Wow this is the epitome of you, you
have captured your own essence perfectly'.

Stick posters on your wall of your favourite
movies and photos that capture the
memories that you never want to forget.
Collect the art you made when you felt most
like yourself. Buy a souvenir from every
place you have the ability to travel to and
arrange them on your refrigerator or your
grandma's refrigerator (or any old random
refrigerator for that matter) or on the
windowsill and allow them to befriend your
house plants. Arrange them messily or let it
be the most organised thing about you, cut
out a picture of a Jensen Interceptor from a
magazine because it happens to be your
favourite car or scribble down Marcus

Aurelias's most thought-provoking quotations and haphazardly Blu Tack it to your ceiling.
Highlight the sentences that stunned you in the books that you were left enraptured by.
Hoard memory boxes and cover the very cardboard of the boxes in train tickets to the place where you created your fondest memories and pictures of the people you created them with.

Have a space of which you are the embodiment.

So, when you feel lost, when you feel close to forgetting who you are, your reminder is there when you lie in bed or reach for milk from your memory-coated fridge.

Invest in yourself

Invest in **you**, don't spend your time and energy being conscious of everyone else's choices in life to determine your next step.

Invest in **you** for the sake of future you.

Pay attention to **your** life, don't become entangled in a mess created by others.

Look after yourself physically, mentally, financially, spiritually, socially.

Strive to be the best version of yourself, make it your long-term goal.

Chapters

Each chapter of your life will pass. Sometimes you will welcome the passing, sometimes you will grieve the passing, and sometimes you forge the passing yourself, for the greater good. Any which way, have faith that this next chapter holds greater things than the last, a fresh set of opportunities, positive additions to your social circle, goals reached, and new goals created, and importantly, acceptance of the past.

Comfort meals

After gathering information from a vast selection of the British public (fellow authors, vegans, those in the catering profession, self-proclaimed soup connoisseurs, those of dual nationality, recipe hoarders, one stray fisherman and various others from all walks of life) I have compiled a list of meals and desserts that provide, to at least one individual, warmth and hospitality in each bite.

Annotate, relate, find inspiration, insert your own additions of comfort meals or if you are that way inclined, laugh maniacally at all suggestions of comfort meals, safe in the knowledge that your own 'go-to' meal is elite, belonging to the top-tier of food and any suggestions, otherwise are to be ridiculed.

Meals that summon floods of gleeful memories or simply are accompanied by instant feelings of safety.

The mention of some specific meals was recurring, some the nation's most beloved...

...some standalone oddities.

The rogue ones (unconventional if you like)

. mushroom stroganoff
. pumpkin & sage baked gnocchi
. naengmyeon (which I have been informed is a North Korean soup)
. cinnamon & raison bagel
. cheesy ramen

Desserts that got a special mention

. profiteroles
. New York cheesecake
. tiramisu
. trifle
. Eton mess
. chocolate brownies
. chocolate cake (most frequently mentioned dessert)
. apple crumble
. sticky toffee pudding
. Biscoff pancakes

Most commonly mentioned (the nation's most beloved)

I won't fail to mention that the vast majority of the following foods were considered not only comfort foods but as suitable hangover easers.
. Big Mac & chips
. ramen
. Sunday dinner
. pizza (variations of which included: Domino's, homemade, pepperoni, and reheated in the morning following a booze-infused night)
. bacon sandwich

. ham & cheese toastie
. mac & cheese
. chippy tea (a personal favourite. Who doesn't love a good grease-filled lump of chips served to you with the finest wooden forks the country has to offer?)
. sushi
. cheese & tomato wrap
. potato waffles
. cheese on toast
. beans on toast
. avocado on toast
. just *toast*
. beef stew & dumplings
. Chinese takeaway (practically the entire menu)
. jacket potato
. cottage pie, Shepherd's Pie, butter pie
. lasagne
. dippy eggs and soldiers
. full English breakfast
. doner kebab
. spaghetti bolognaise
. tomato soup with crusty bread

A section dedicated to sausage in all forms
. sausage roll
. sausage & mash
. sausage & roast potatoes
. sausage ragu
. cocktail sausages
. sausage casserole

For when life inevitably gets messy, jot down your own comfort foods:

.

.

(a note to the individual who said margarine by the spoonful: when they say 'embrace your quirks' this is the one quirk I would **not** be rushing to embrace)

Woolf's Wisest Words

"Books are the mirrors of the soul." – **Virginia Woolf**

"sleep, that deplorable curtailment of the joy of life." – *Virginia Woolf*

"I have a deeply hidden and inarticulate desire for something beyond the daily life" – **Virginia Woolf**

"My brain hums with scraps of poetry and madness." – **Virginia Woolf**

"I am made and remade continually. Different people draw different words from me." – **Virginia Woolf**

"No need to hurry. No need to sparkle. No need to be anybody but oneself." – **Virginia Woolf**

"When you consider things like the stars, our affairs don't seem to matter very much, do they?" – **Virginia Woolf**

Glamorisation

In this world there are a great many things that should not be glamorised, sugar-coated or romanticised, and yet time and time again the public, the media and idle gossipers do exactly that.

Serial killers, mental illness, poverty, infidelity: a few of many things that tend to be harmfully romanticised.

However, glamorising your own life, behaving as if you are the main character in a magnificently formed, well thought-out, brilliantly-directed film, forces an appreciation of every small, beautiful detail of your existence.

If it makes you happy, you owe no explanation.

Decision fatigue

When everyone is seemingly waiting for your decision...

...no matter what
decision you make,
it will inevitably be the
wrong decision in somebody's eyes.

Say yes.
Say no.
Say fuck it.
Go to university.
Fuck the education system, travel while you can.
Vote Labour.
Vote Conservative.
Fuck the government.
You should lose some weight.
You should gain some weight.
You should make that decision for yourself.
Be somebody.
Be nobody.
Be *whoever the fuck you want.*
Decide *whatever the fuck you want.*

Why you are you

Never believe that you only hold value
because you work 48 hours a week or
because you can spell
supercalifragilisticexpialidoscious correctly
every time without fail or because you made
something of yourself despite multiple rough
patches, or because you are the best
equestrian in your region. Don't attach your
value as a human being to your
achievements.
You are worthy.
You are valuable.
You are 99% composed of approximately 6
elements:
Oxygen, hydrogen, nitrogen, carbon, calcium
and phosphorous...
All of which began as atoms spat out in
supernovae.
That is why you are of value: no external
validation is required.
You don't deserve the things that you
deserve solely because of your occupation or
morals or life achievements, you deserve
them for being you.
Managing to be a beautifully unique entity
when in fact you are composed no differently
than any other human.

An extremely short list of places to visit

- **Shitterton,** Dorset (speaks for itself really.)

- **The Shambles,** York. Mesmerising year-round, though especially mesmerising in the winter months, with its market stalls, spectacular light displays, cozy teepees and cobbled streets. The film Harry Potter, took a lot of inspiration from York, 'Diagon Alley' being a magic-infused recreation of the Shambles. York itself is a must-visit... previously home to the Vikings and Romans and now home to chocolate factories and100s of quaint little shops dotted between haunted pubs and Roman ruins.

- **Puffin island,** Anglesey. From April to July, you stand a fair chance of witnessing puffins nesting. Mesmerising to say the least.

Do everything in
your power to
protect your
peace.

Permission

If, like me, you grant yourself permission to do certain things depending on the day: STOP.

You are allowed to treat yourself.
You are allowed to feel good about yourself, whether it's a Friday or a Monday.

For a lot of people, Friday signifies a break from business; subsequently a takeaway pizza is deserved. Whilst this is still true, you should treat and congratulate yourself for making it through a week. Treating yourself should be a necessity.

You are forever working, helping, bettering yourself or simply just *being*. And just existing is something to celebrate, not just on your allocated Friday or Saturday.

So, go and have a relaxing bath on a Tuesday.
Or put some money in Subway's pocket on a Sunday or go and get your weekly pint or few on a Wednesday instead.

You have full permission to treat yourself for simply still existing despite everything.

Money

Money always finds its way back to you.
But not all life experiences will do the same.

Boundaries

If, by setting boundaries, you find yourself losing people around you – those whom you cherish – then the relationship you had with them was unhealthy.

Just like parting with that lovely pair of jeans that no longer fit you, setting boundaries summons 'a spring clean' of the people you associate yourself with, allowing space to seek a brand new, more vibrant, more practical, more *you*... pair of jeans or group of acquaintances.

Unplanned

Often the unplanned yields a greater result than the planned.

The universe, time, peas & your irrelevance

You are irrelevant.
Your decisions are irrelevant.
Your mistakes are irrelevant.
Your missed opportunities are irrelevant.

Time

Demographers have estimated that 109 billion humans have come before us, over the past 192,000 years
(**onehunderedandninetytwothousand**)
109 billion humans have lived, breathed, made drunken mistakes, been victim to infidelity, kissed the wrong person, failed exams, lost friends.

Including the current population, 117 billion people have existed, which means that amongst a sea of mistakes and questionable decisions made by nearly all of these individuals, you are irrelevant.

Life is so excruciatingly short, so who in their right mind would dwell on their past and their failures?

Seize every single day that you are blessed with on this planet, do whatever you want with your life and worry less, because **you** are irrelevant. The sad but freeing reality is that you inevitably will be forgotten, so take that knowledge and do

w h a t e v e r

you want. Presuming you are at peak health, and you make it to the grand age of 100, your 100 years is minuscule in comparison with the time that humans have inhabited the planet so far and the years following your existence that humans will continue to inhabit earth in.

The universe

Pre-warning of sciency-shit upcoming.
What is observable to the human race, (through futuristic-feeling technology that I will never quite wrap my head around) is 27.4 billion light years' worth of universe.

For reference: a lightyear is equivalent to roughly 6 trillion miles (6,000,000,000,000 miles)

There are roughly 200 billion galaxies in the universe...
One of those galaxies is home to 3,916 solar systems...
One of those solar systems is home to

PLANET EARTH

Our solar system alone is 333,346 times bigger
in mass than our little planet...

I mention this to reinforce how truly irrelevant
you are, how irrelevant I am, how irrelevant
Einstein (one of the most influential people to
have recently existed) was.
How irrelevant your thoughts,
actions and
behaviours are.

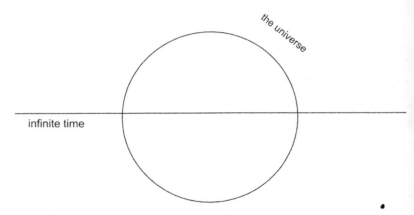

the universe

infinite time

you: a pea sized spec
of irrelevance that goes
by the name of 'life'

This diagram does not accurately portray the sheer enormity of your irrelevance, nor does it appropriately show how big the universe really is.

So, the main take away from this is that you are irrelevant but in the most beautiful way possible, in a way that allows you to be truly free and untangle yourself from all your woes.

You are given one life, so fight to keep it. Find safety in the knowledge that your existence will not impact upon the universe or the passing of time, meaning your life is yours to live unapologetically.

Control

- If it's something you cannot possibly control, don't stress about it. That's not to say you shouldn't feel your feelings, just don't allow yourself to ruminate on them.
- Whatever will be, will be.
- Some things in life are going to be beyond your control, don't let that fact set you back.
- There are other aspects of your life that you can control with positive outcomes, so let this one go.

'Great minds think alike'

A statement that couldn't be more wrong. It is my belief that the greatest minds think inordinately different thoughts from one and another. No two great minds think exactly alike, or else they do not meet the criteria for a 'great mind'.

You are vital to someone.
You are vital to someone.
You are vital to someone.
You are vital to someone.
You are vital to someone.
You are vital to someone.
You are vital to someone.

Finding small comforts

Finding comfort and inner peace doesn't have to manifest itself in you taking up hobbies labelled as 'hippie'. You don't have to master yoga, the downward-facing dog or the bhujangasana.

You just need to start seeking a peaceful mindset and laying out all things that comfort and soothe your brain.

Comfort can be derived from many things, all of which can be deeply personal to you or generic and applicable to the majority.

To aid yourself best, a toolkit of material items and mental practices that provide peace and calm is ideal.

Which basic comforts will help to bring you back to the moment rather than enable you to dive deeper into the vast waters of unease within you?

In case you cannot think for yourself here are a few suggestions of some general and some oddly specific comforts:
Photos of your childhood, instant noodles, that one oversized hoodie splattered with

stubborn stains, guided meditation, calming playlists, hot chocolate with whipped cream and marshmallows, The Simpsons theme tune, Mary Berry's 'fresh strawberry tartlet' recipe, lavender nighttime spray, white noise, Christmas films, the knowledge that a chippy tea awaits you at home, trips to your local garden centre, fluffy socks, rediscovering your love for Blur, big hugs, online shopping for cutlery, reading Vogue, watching sunrises, hiking in the rain with a promise of fresh bread and homemade soup once you return to your house, lava lamps, late night cereal, reading books like these, word searches, colouring, knitted blankets, trampolining, newly washed sheets, the smell of aftershave, foods that melt on your tongue, Season 3 of Friends, filling up birthday piñatas, reminiscing about camping trips in Dorset, writing letters, Kentucky Fried Chicken, fireflies practising calligraphy, pondering how friendly the owners of your local Chinese takeaway are, amethyst, Spongebob Squarepants, pressing flowers, hot water bottles, duck-themed bedrooms, seeking out the next staple piece in your wardrobe, getting your hair cut, watching videos of cats, Origami, calling your favourite relative… the list is endless.

Spinal aches and intuition

If you happened to have an ache in your spine, you'd be aware that something was amiss, but not sure what. You can't see your own spine. It would take another to point out to you that the reason for your discomfort was a bruise covering your spine.
In the same breath – if you were in a friendship, relationship, or any situation where something in your mind was nagging at you – it might take someone else to point out what you can't see.

Jigsaw

You may think you are no longer whole: people chipped away at you, experiences eroded you.
You may feel you are a walking shell of what you once where and what you could've been.
You may *know* that you are a visual representation of wasted potential.

It is easy to think that way when you have been broken time and time again – your mind is corrupt with overwhelming nothingness with a dash of overbearing pain. When the authentic version of you, so majestic, so full of love and laughter and sweet nectar-like innocence has been pulled apart and vulgarly incinerated before your eyes, it is easy to think you may never be whole again.

But you are a jigsaw, every second you have spent fighting, every time you say goodbye to the toxicity that tries to creep into your bones, has built you up that little bit more, slotted jigsaw pieces back into a place unbeknownst to you.
Every smile from a stranger.
Every new hobby you've picked up.
Every time you've indulged in nostalgia of the good old days before fractions of you began to disappear.
Every new song you discover.

Every time you dance hand in hand with your soulmate, with no concern for the outside world.

Every time you read a new book that provides a hundred new perspectives on life and love and pain.

Every time you speak to yourself tenderly, dismissing the rage you feel for becoming an incomplete entity.

Every time you make someone laugh.

Every time you love someone, be it only for a fleeting second or the remainder of your life.

You are rebuilding yourself; you are adding new jigsaw pieces to what was once crumbling, devastatingly disintegrating.

And when, inevitably, you find something has chipped away at you yet again, and you want to give in and return to your most fragile state as a shell who merely observes the world, too frail to participate, remember all you have done that has slowly rebuilt you. All the odd jigsaw pieces here and there that recreated you cannot be disregarded.

Maybe now you are a jigsaw consisting of pieces from 8,000 different jigsaws – *that* does not equal broken or not whole, it equals imperfect.

Imperfect is perfectly fine.
We are all imperfect.

<u>You are...</u>

you are loved, you are safe
You are loved, you are safe
you are loved, you are safe
you are loved, you are safe
you are loved, you are safe
you are loved,
you are safe.

Beetroot

Some people willingly eat beetroot, a fact you have to accept in order to move on with your life.

Calming playlist

(a selection of the songs that bring me
instant peace of mind)
. (Sittin' On) the Dock of the Bay – Otis
Redding
. Vienna – Billy Joel
. Scott Street – Phoebe Bridgers
. Big Black Car – Gregory Alan Isakov
. Photograph – Ed Sheeran
. Love is an Accident – Flyte
. Two Ghosts – Harry Styles
. Cowboy like me – Taylor Swift
. Truly Madly Deeply – Yoke Lore
. Growing Sideways – Noah Kahan
. Cloudbusting – Kate Bush
. Ho Hey – The Lumineers
. Freakin' Out On the Interstate – Briston
Maroney
. '74-'75 – The Connells
. Hotel California – Eagles
. The Night We Met – Lord Huron
. Sparks – Coldplay
. Wash. – Bon Iver
. All the Pretty Girls – KALEO
. Talk Tonight – Oasis
. Heaven – Brian Adams
. Last Request – Paulo Nutini
. Baby Can I Hold You – Tracy Chapman
. Male Fantasy – Billie Eilish

<u>Comfort songs</u>.

Consult your Spotify playlists and pluck out the songs that summon serenity. Play them whilst you clean, cook, read, journal, work out, shower – or simply just embrace the effect of the song whilst pondering life tucked up in bed.

Unicorn

If Scotland selected the unicorn as their national animal, any ludicrous decision you make is a ridiculously normal decision in comparison. So go forth and make 'out there' decisions and statements.

Naked roll matt

Perhaps one of the most humbling human experiences is going to insult someone, and in the process, tripping up on your meticulously planned words that aim to stab.
I was once on the receiving end of, 'Shut up you look like a naked roll matt,'
as opposed to a naked mole rat, an actual creature.
Safe to say, the malicious intent was undone, and the sender became a laughing stock.

The Rain

Let the rain cleanse your messy head, allow
the downpour to untangle the messy
thoughts that trouble your poor brain.
Do so in your preferred way:
Dance in the rain,
Stand solemnly in the middle of a field
letting fast-falling rain drops slap your bare
arms.
Or create an aesthetically appealing corner of
autumn scented candles, Norwegian-looking
blankets, euphoric music and listen intently
to the rain as it blends with your music.

Running

People will often warn you not to run away from your problems, but sometimes running away is the one thing you can do to help yourself. Don't be naïve and believe that your problems will never arise again. Running is a temporary fix. Sometimes, though, it is the break you need.

A mildly chilling bedtime read, that should be partnered with external warmth such as hot chocolate and roaring hearths.

(That doesn't leave you needing to read the next chapter, forcing you to stay awake longer than is ideal, purely because the story only consists of one chapter.)

Her hands submerged in the soil.
Her only happy place.
Her only escape.
Rows upon rows of tulips and nasturtiums lay sporadically placed between rows of asparagus, radishes, carrots, and lettuce in ten varying shades of green. Her personal favourite was an oak sapling that stood in solitude, casting an evening shadow over her as she tended to her radishes.
Protecting her.
Protecting her from the horrors of her life in captivity.
Her life as a prisoner in a crumbling marriage and a husband who couldn't let go.

Mentally...
...he destroyed her, suffocated her, rinsed the air of anything

breathable.

The constant belittling. His judgemental nature. His means of making her doubt her entire existence.
It started with small comments:
'Clara, my darling, I can't let you leave the house looking such a state.'
Such comments eventually morphed to, a simple:
'Clara, my darling, I can't let you leave the house.'

'You're mine forever, Clara.'

Forever.

F o r e v e r.

F o r e v e r.

To start with, she complied.
Days filled with dancing to the greatest 80s hits.
Hoovering in time to Duran Duran tracks.
Baking scones with Bonnie Tyler's voice as company, waiting for her husband's return from work.
Heaven.
But six months into so-called heaven, she craved the feeling of a soft breeze cooling her at the ankles, wrapping itself around her,

embracing her. She missed the smell of the earth. The satisfaction of watching a tomato redden over the slow passing of time. Waking up, once so easy, became a chore, getting through a week was a gruelling monotonous task, designed to expend every last drip of energy that remained in her.

The simple things...

The simple things, were what she missed,
were what she begged for,
'Just 5 minutes in the garden, please.'

'No.'
No was always the answer.
Until it wasn't.
Until something mellowed inside him.

'Clara darling, forgive me.'

Days quickly became full of plants and seeds and flowers and trees and fruits and bees.

Each day, with its fresh list of demands, became more and more wearisome. Over days and weeks and months of a forced hibernation at the hand of another it became apparent to her that people are like weeds, they entwine themselves in the existence of others. They can quickly corrupt your mind.

They rule your life and claw cruelly at your happiness.

They make life a misery.

Just as a weed makes itself a home in a flowerbed, to bring chaos, disruption, and misery there.

Tormenting the tulips
Bullying the bluebells
Angering the azaleas
Slowly but surely killing off the entire flowerbed.

And once they are there, they are there. There is no way off ridding them from the place they make home.

He was a weed. A nasty spiteful weed unable to let go of her.
Weeds, however, by nature, can be beautiful.

Beautiful & deceptive.

Foxglove,
for example. A shade of purple so bright that you might stop to ask why such a colour was present in the scones your wife had spent the afternoon lovingly baking and plating up. But he didn't.

On the evening of 1st June, she baked
scones with Bonnie Tyler's voice for
company.
Flour,
butter,
sugar,
milk,
foxglove.

The beautifully deceptive foxglove, that had
been growing as long as her silent hatred for
him.

Now she could be submerged fully in her
safe place. Her body and the earth could be
at one in the comfort of a wooden box
alongside him.

In sync, they took a bite.

'Forever's gonna start tonight'.

Pen and paper people

You are certain to have the best
conversations with those who keep a pen
and paper by their bed.

Personification of a place

It is nearly impossible to heal in a place that broke you, an environment that cast misery over your forthcoming years of human-hood.

A positive act of retaliation:
become so drastically opposed to such place, that you and he are impossibly incomparable.

Marcus Aurelius himself said that **'The best revenge is to be unlike him who performed the injury'.**

Be unlike the territory that gave rise to your downfall.

That will be the ascent of the best version of you. The sweet 'revenge' Aurelius speaks of is, in fact, healing, despite the relentless pain which that place inflicted on you.

So, personify that place, make (it) him or her, a replica of Lucifer or the Grinch or the politician whose words grate on you most or your Year 11 Biology teacher, and strive to be everything they are not.

<u>Follow at least **one** of the following sets of instructions:</u>

Take your book, go and make a brew and relax with your book and brew.

Take your book, cook up masterfully-made instant noodles and relax with your noodles and book.

Take your book, run a bath, and relax with your book and bath.

Take your book, gather up some stray pens and illustrate, annotate, and colour your book.

Take your book, do something for yourself. Look after your book and yourself.

Alternatively, get some sleep.

Jam and Cream

Depending where you are from, your views on condiment layering on a scone will vary. Also depending on where you are from, it would be a lot more than insulting to go against the majority in this matter, an offence punishable by expulsion from your postcode.

No matter which way you apply your jam and cream to your scone, there is little if any difference taste-wise in the end result.

Make this applicable to life – do what you want in whatever order you want, allow yourself to prioritise and the end result shouldn't be too different from what it could have been if you hadn't skipped a step or put it second in the queue of priorities. You may find that you achieved your end goal in record time because of the tweaks in structure, or maybe you find everything took that little bit longer and you needed that extra time. Or perhaps, contrary to all your deep-rooted beliefs that cream comes first followed by jam, you decided to spread the metaphorical jam on to your life and in doing so realised you never needed the cream.

Yes, this defeats my point about the end result never being drastically different, but the absence of cream, in my eyes, does not come under the category of 'drastic' changes.

FYI. Jam then cream is perfect (try not to boycott my book because of this statement)

HYGGE
[hue-gah] Danish

The ritual of embracing cosiness and a comfortable conviviality leading to an overall contentment and a well state of mind.

Eternal soul, mortal body

The most freeing advice I can give – the thought that helped me reframe my views on mortality, my body, and my soul – is to be found on this page. This section, I thought, needed, and deserved, pages and pages of articulate writing and in-depth explanations, but I have come to realise it is more easily digested as a bite-sized lump of thought-provoking words rather than a full 3-course meal of thought-provoking literature for you to eventually choke on:

I am in love with the notion,
That our souls are eternal.
Our bodies, merely mortal vessels,
That house said soul with its attached,
Fiery chaos, beauty, and liveliness.

What a marvellous house your body is.

Make your *own* choices

A true artist creates not what will most
appeal to critics or what is most fit for public
consumption, rather the outlandish, the
beautiful, the ugly, the painful, the dramatic
that lives hidden deep in the coves of their
mind.

Consider this when making choices. Are you
aiming to appeal to the critics in your life or
are you making the decision that comes from
deep within your mind and soul?

Stop expecting too much from the seasons

Living in these days of media overload it is easy to fall victim to the cult of comparison. You want the same summer as that Barbie and Ken-looking couple, who seemingly spend the entirety of their summer jet skiing and laughing and exploring and on expensive yachts and who are so deeply (nauseatingly) in love. They are seemingly so far removed from your life. The picture-perfect image they uphold may well be a façade, that bikini body may be photoshopped, those smiles may be fake, but it doesn't stop us longing for the perfection that they seemingly achieve. All of a sudden you become fixated on HAVING to have intense heat and endless days of sun to toast in, not one inch of burnt skin, pub garden trips daily, at least ten different rivers and lakes to jump into, ice cream vans at your disposal, late nights around a fire before returning to your allocated tent, summer flings, a trip to Kos, Rhodes, Malaga and Ibiza.

Even if your perfect summer is drastically far removed from the above mentioned 'summer ideal', chances are you still expect a lot from the summer (whether that be down to the influence of others or not). It is great to have plans and goals no matter what season we are entering. However, when (unwittingly) creating this subconscious list of expectations, you are setting yourself up for an upset in the aftermath of a summer that didn't meet all your requirements.

Of course, this applies to all seasons; the vast majority of Brits hold their breath in anticipation of a white Christmas. Maybe your winter *has* to be snow-filled to the brim, with cozy film nights and hot chocolate with a ludicrous number of marshmallows. Maybe your winter is a write-off in the absence of 100% success in present-giving and receiving. Maybe you actually look forward to the in-laws turning up.

Your expectations are sabotaging your chance of enjoying the seasons and the things they bring to the table each year.

Perhaps you didn't eat toffee apples in such quantities that you could not ever, bear to look at them, or maybe you did not step back into your childhood – collecting conkers – but while you were busy chasing your season-specific occurrences, you forgot to pay attention to the cozy nights in front of your TV, with a chunky-knit blanket weighing down your legs and those rainy days spent inside with the smell of your favourite 'cinnamon bun' candle infusing the house.

Thieves

There is a common misconception that death
is the ultimate thief.

Death, with or without reason, fairly or
unfairly, achieves the task laid out for him.
He is a mere worker.

Self sabotage, in reality, is the thief of all
potential and happiness...

and potential happiness.

Why you should calm the fuck down

It is an unfortunate reality that most of us are all too well acquainted with the effects of anxiety and stress, both of which might reduce our longevity and quality of life.
We often look past all the symptoms of an overactive nervous system, 'it is *just* stress' or 'it is *just* anxiety'.
But is it ever *just*?
That persistent headache? Constant low mood, sleep disturbances? Dental concerns? Digestive issues? Intense fatigue?
These are all symptoms that can skulk into your life with such stealth that you might not make a connection between your headache-y, dentally-ill, sleep-deprived state and an over-worked, over-active nervous system.
To combat such things, long-term lifestyle changes are often required. However, in the short term there are a number of effective methods that aid in the calming of the nervous system. I will spare you the scientific reasoning behind each, because if you'd wanted a science-y book, I presume you would have opted for one of the many scientific books Waterstones has to offer rather that this rambly little book.

<u>Things to calm your nervous system:</u>

. application of heat (hot water bottles, hot drinks, hot baths, heat packs, hot showers)

. weighted vests, blankets, and stuffed toys

. breathing exercises and meditation (park your scepticism here and try it... trust me just try it)

. aromatherapy (dig out those essential oils, bought for you many Christmases ago, untouched still)

. cold exposure (sucking ice cubes, ice packs, ice baths, cold showers)

. healthy fats, or any fats for that matter, (the properties of fatty foods are suggested to strengthen the protective layer around nerve cells... I will stop with the science now)

. relaxing music

. **Sleep.**

Miscellaneous items

Sometimes the universe misplaces its miscellaneous objects and dumps them in your life. Often the misplacement of such things will cease to have any effect on the trajectory of your life. For example, the rogue tortoise I found in my hedge one summer: *it* had no positive or negative influence on the way my life was going.

However, sometimes you find yourself walking the path of life and the universe has inconveniently mislaid a marble which turns up in your shoe, creating negative side effects.
So, check your shoes and give them a shake, and while you're at it, check your metaphorical shoes and give them a shake too.

You could if you wanted to

You could if you wanted to.
If your heart most desired, you could.
You **could** run 5 miles with the earth
beneath your feet.
You could become one with the sea,
doing backflips into serene waters,
summer-long.
You could fall in love with fire,
be **it** late night bonfires with bottles of beer
and the buzz of fireflies or the fire in your
soul ignited by imagination.
You could soar through the air, **all** woes
abandoned when your feet leave the ground:
Rollercoasters,
Zip wires,
Precarious rope swings,
　　　　　you could do it all.

Childhood

A lot of us yearn for our childhoods to return. Childhood becomes a distant memory in the midst of corporate jobs, financial strain and remembering to walk the dog.

We crave and worship the summer year-round but maybe sometimes it is that sweet childhood summer that we actually crave when the reek of nostalgia sets in and all of a sudden we are saddened (by the realisation) that we are no longer kids. Anatomically, maybe we will never return to our playful, delightful, youthful selves.

But who said you can't be a fairy or a pirate or a werewolf or a mermaid from time to time?

It could be worse, eh?

It could be worse: you could be hours away from seeing any familiar face and hooked up to a bag of fluids in an accident and emergency room that smells of decay. You might be reaching a point beyond mere starvation with a strong mind that, justifiably, won't allow you to pay £6 for a simple tub of Pringles. You might also be with an ensemble of bloodied-up drunks, shouting the odds and filling up sick buckets, in every sheer curtain-walled room surrounding you.

And if you are in that exact situation, it could be worse: you could be in that same situation in a hospital that is rapidly burning to the ground.

Take the chance

I could tell you that opportunities will
always arise for *at least* a second time. But
if I did, it would be a lie.
I want this book to be full of simple truths
and what's more I want all of my words to
hold some credibility so that when I say,
'This darkness will pass' you will believe me.
So, I won't lie to you: opportunities *do,*
frequently, rise again,
but it is never guaranteed.
Take every opportunity offered to you on the
off chance that it won't come back around.
Don't let regret consume you because you
held yourself back every time you were given
any chance.
Take the chance.

Letter writing

Dear Reader,
Put aside your feud with the Post Office and the ever-ascending price of stamps, alongside the view that in this most technologically advanced era letter-writing *ought to be* obsolete.
Hand-written letters are thought to have first come about as early as 500 BC, a crucial part of official and non-official communication to this day.
The art of letter-writing is at risk of extinction, replaced by emailing, messaging, calling and facetiming, all extremely convenient. But sometimes receiving a good old-fashioned letter can create a priceless smile on the face of the recipient.
So, in the name of keeping letter writing alive I shall include some ideas of things to include in a letter to your chosen reader.
Keep your reader updated, tell them about what's new in life, about your recent trip to Sweden, about your new pet parakeet, or that pair of shoes bought for you at Christmas that you adore.
Ask about them and their life; be intrigued.
Add small tokens: photos, perfume or aftershave samples, flattened origami, pressed flowers, quotes and lyrics, stickers and your own doodles, postcards, recipes...

anything envelope-sized to be honest, with the exception of a few things... because, personally I'd rather not receive a flattened, pancake-like toilet roll, despite the fact that it probably falls into the 'envelope-sized' bracket.

Lots of love and best regards,

From Grace

Fleetwood to Faro

Fasten the belt in your favourite,
'54 Ford Versaille,
From your little town of Fleetwood,
Fly down the motorway.

Blast a coming-of-age song,
and realise you've come of age.
Find yourself at Folkestone,
Ready to start a new page.

Fond memories of your hometown,
As the Eurostar makes its way,
To France where you are free to drive,
To Dinant, Bern or Pompeii.

Find a route to Faro,
Cross the borders into Spain,
And ponder how fond you are,
Of the idea of starting again.

Now you are far from home,
Seventeen-hundred miles away.
But you've learned and laughed and lived;
memories that can't be taken away.

Rhubarb & Custard

A recipe that should relieve some stress if you ever find yourself in the unlikely position that a particularly posh, affluent individual springs a cocktail party on you with expectations of concoctions of your finest liqueurs your fridge has to offer.

To make 6, you will need:
>450g chopped rhubarb
>130g sugar
>120ml water
>150ml vodka
>50ml advocaat
>120ml lemonade or tonic
>A sprinkle of nutmeg

1. Before starting the syrup-making process, put six cocktail glasses in the freezer to chill. Create a syrup by putting both the caster sugar and water in a saucepan, maintaining a low heat, ensuring the water doesn't bubble but allowing for the sugar to dissolve.

2. Once the sugar is no longer visible, turn the heat up slightly and add the chopped rhubarb, cover the saucepan with a lid and leave for five minutes to simmer.

3. Pour the mixture into a sieve and squash the rhubarb until all the juice is out,

then pour your pulp-free creation back into the pan and boil for 2-4 minutes. You should now be left with a 'homemade rhubarb syrup' (which sounds rather impressive if the guests happen to be particularly snobby). Leave to cool in a fridge – any fridge, grandma's refrigerator perhaps.

4. Shake the vodka and 150ml of the rhubarb together and as much or as little ice as you want, then strain this into your chilled or near-frozen cocktail glasses.

5. Whisk together the advocaat and lemonade/tonic. Per glass, steadily pour 25ml of the mixture over an upturned spoon to make sure it floats on top of the contents of the glass.

6. Dust with nutmeg and serve with a side of rhubarb and custard sweets or if that might be considered overly rhubarb-y for your palate, acquire the finest cupcakes that you can find.

7. Impress all six guests and in true British fashion, get absolutely **wasted!**

(No tequila) sunrise

An easy five minute non-alcoholic (still impressive looking), completely different tasting alternative to the rhubarb and custard cocktail. Suitable for use in any situation when a fancy-looking drink is required but your guests consist of non-drinkers or ten-year-olds who like the idea of a cocktail.

To make six, you will need:
>450ml orange juice
>450ml lemonade/sparkling water/non-alcoholic wine
>6tbsp of grenadine
>6 orange slices

This recipe is painfully foolproof, so try not to mess it up.

1. Grab six standard Champagne glasses and pour 75ml of orange juice into each, followed by 75ml of non-alcoholic wine (the preferable option), sparkling water or lemonade.
2. Slightly tilt each glass and pour in a tbsp of grenadine.
3. Garnish with an orange slice and drink with your posh friends without the threat of embarrassing decisions being made... well, without the threat of alcohol-

induced embarrassing decisions... I can't promise you won't soberly embarrass yourself anyway.

Out of the loop

Being out of the loop can be a blessing. Despite the devastating loneliness that can creep up on you as a result of being 'out of the loop', sometimes it is best to keep yourself to yourself in order to preserve your happiness and sense of self.

Unpredictable

Embrace the unpredictability of what life has in store for you, feel safe in knowing that it will all work out eventually, the universe always has something better in mind for your future. There is no point in tiring yourself out with monotonous chasing of a future that is not set in stone. Rather, let it find its way to you.

Stop being afraid

Stop being afraid of what could go wrong and focus on the beauty of not knowing what *is* going to go right.

Stop being **afraid** of what **could** go **wrong** and focus on the **beauty** of **not knowing** what *is* going to **go right**.

Stop being afraid of what could go wrong and focus on the beauty of not knowing what *is* going to go right.

Funeral

At your funeral, people will not recall how your body looked. People will not speak of how many mistakes you made.

People are going to remember the songs you loved, the times you made them smile, the way you had a habit of twirling your hair, that one time you went down a water slide backwards and came off it grinning ear to ear. People will remember how you only used kids' toothpaste because it tasted of strawberries and how you had such an intense love for seeing the world.

Do not fall into the trap of thinking that people only notice your appearance and wrongdoing in life. People will remember your fiery soul, your quirks, and your big heart.

Potential Essentials

(A written concoction of the small potential essentials, to keep on your person, in your car or in your room.)

Plasters and bandages,
Wipes,
Sweets for drops in your blood sugar levels
(or just general consumption),
Pen and paper,
A spare earring back,
Needle and thread,
A spare tampon for yourself or whomever may require it,
A lighter,
A water filter,
Antihistamines,
A water bottle,
A penknife,
Headphones (for those tortuously long car journeys)

Swearing

Depending on who you are and what beliefs you hold, swearing can only ever be classed as vulgar, crude, and unnecessary. That opinion is valid, completely.

All I have to say on the topic of swearing is that some of the truly most wildly astute people I have encountered, from all sectors of society have fucking loved swearing every once in a while: doctors, teachers, cleaners, forensic scientists, business owners, solicitors, morticians, psychologists, motivational speakers, cheese makers. A shit ton of people from all professions essentially.

you

    you will only exist once.
   There will only ever be one _you._
Within the vast amount of people who
existed _before_
 and those who will exist
after you,
 not one of them is or was a replica of you.
So, embrace your body,
       your mind,
         your heart,
          your soul.
Because there will only ever be one of each of
them and that is what makes you so
Irrevocably valuable.

A random array of facts to impress your dinner party guests with

(That is of course if you have any dinner guests besides your four-legged companions, who I don't think would be too impressed with these facts.)
I find that it is always handy to have a few miscellaneous facts on standby in case you are ambushed and forced to hold or attend a quiz.

1. The famous 'Spanish Steps' are located in Rome, Italy.

2. Amazon, the company, was previously named 'Cadabra'.

3. The gestation period for an African elephant is 22 months.

4. The circulatory system, if laid out flat, would exceed 60,000 miles in length.

5. Due to a thermal change that prompts a reaction in its iron structure, the height of the Eiffel tower increases in the summer.

6. The hashtag symbol's real name is an octothorpe.

7. Archaeologists found that the famous heads on Easter Island do, in fact, have bodies submerged in the ground, therefore unseen.

8. Russia has a bigger surface area than Pluto.

9. Saint Lucia is the only country in the world named after a woman.

10. There are currently over 10,000 different varieties of grapes.

11. A 'jiffy' is an actual measurement of time.

12. Queen Elizabeth II was a trained mechanic.

13. A mayfly holds the record for the animal with the shortest lifespan, each one only living up to 24 hours.

14. Maine is the only US state that contains just one syllable.

15. Three of Henry VIII's wives shared the name 'Catherine'.

Drastic differences

You are constructed of flesh, blood, and all of
your quirks. You are you; you are so
enormously different from every other
human.

Belly of the whale

If you ever find yourself trapped in an
elevator, be thankful you are only trapped in
an **elevator** rather than the belly of a whale.
I imagine the inside of a whale isn't blessed
with elevator music, rather, masses of late,
lamented krill...
silver linings...
Stomach linings.

DO WITH THIS PAGE,
WHATEVER YOU MOST DESIRE.
RANT, JOURNAL, SCRIBBLE,
EAT IT, USE AS A FACE CLOTH,
CREATE A MAKESHIFT
BIRTHDAY CARD, UTILISE AS A
PAINT PALETTE, PRESS
FLOWERS, WRITE OUT YOUR
SHOPPING LIST, SERVE
YOURSELF A PIZZA SLICE ON IT,
DRAW A MASTERPIECE, FILL
WITH POINTLESS ANGRY
SCRIBBLES, WRITE A LIST OF
HELPLINES AND THEIR MOBILE
NUMBERS FOR YOUR MOMENTS
OF NEED
...THE POSSIBILITIES ARE
ENDLESS.

10 types of people not to trust

(Since I dedicated a few pages to the types of people in life you won't regret trusting, I thought it fitting to write a list of types of people you shouldn't trust. I didn't want to leave you in a pool of naivety, thinking everyone was trustworthy. Of course, there are the obvious people you shouldn't trust, like Hitler-worshippers or serial killers. The examples I am about to share are the underdogs, the ones you would expect complete innocence from.)

1. Those who do not read literature.
2. The parents of a child under the age of 25 named Gary.
3. Anyone with a condescending disposition. (If an individual has it in them to remain constantly condescending who knows what other dark traits lurk within them)
4. Those who can crack their neck on command (what's to say they won't crack your neck on command)
5. Those who buy a car purely for the badge and in doing so dismiss functionality and convenience (these individuals think only on the surface level and tend to believe in their own warped logic and cannot be told otherwise. I can think of many situations where these traits would deem them untrustworthy)

6. People who turn their noses up at the idea of a book like this, or worse, at the idea of any book.
7. Those who enjoy jellied eels.
8. Those non-Americans who spell any and everything the American way. e.g., color, humor, gray.
9. Those who feed bread to the ducks.
10. Whoever wrote the bus timetable that tells me that my bus will be here in five minutes when in fact it I am on my second hour of awaiting my bus that has been 'five minutes away' the whole two hours, as I write these very words.

——URGENT——

Take this warning as seriously as you would an **earthquake warning** or a **flood warning** or a 'you've been in contact with someone who has tested positive for **COVID-19'**. Or 'warning, the **in-laws** are going to be joining you for Christmas'.

I **urge** you to **travel**.

Do it young, do it old,
Do it depressed, do it ecstatic,
Do it alone, do it with hundreds,
Do it when skint, do it once you've won the lottery.

Just, **please**, do it.
See the world, because there is so much beyond what you have seen.
There are so many memories lined up and waiting for you, so many intriguing people, traditions, cuisines...

Instructions
1. Book the ticket
2. Take the step
3. **Don't look back.**

Dog ear

A book can only ever be classified as 'ruined' when it is an exquisite plot written awfully or an awful plot written exquisitely – those are the only two times a book is ruined.

You are not 'ruining' a book by dog-earing the pages that compelled you to get up and do something great, so that next time you find yourself in a slump you know where to turn to for that much needed motivator and reminder that you are capable of greatness.

You are not 'ruining' a book by dog-earing the pages that made you feel empowered.

You are not 'ruining' a book by dog-earing. the page that served you a slab of comfort and reminded you of how far you have come.

The beauty of a book is that the content doesn't change, the world will revolve, night becomes day becomes night, new world leaders are introduced, people are born, and people are buried. But the words marked in a book remain the same, maybe over time their meaning changes or becomes more relevant or not relevant at all... those words remain the same even with the passing of time. Therefore, no action you take can ruin or erase those words and the beauty within them.

You are not 'ruining' a book by highlighting and annotating as I have suggested you do with this very book or by dog-earing the pages written so movingly that your tear stains now morph the

last few words

So can you

How many others have shared that same thought that you ruminate on so tirelessly: 'I can *not* do this anymore', and then proceeded to *do it* anyway?

How many people are LIVING and breathing around you who once couldn't think of anything worse than living and breathing?

If they can live and breathe with peace of mind, so can you.

"I took a deep breath and listened to the old brag of my heart. I am, I am, I am."

– **Sylvia Plath, The Bell Jar**

<u>Questions to ask yourself in order to discover</u>
the real you.

- How do you spend a 'lazy day'?
- What limits you most in life?
- If you were to have 3 wishes granted, what would they be?
- What are you most grateful for?
- What are your 5 favourite possessions?
- Who do you look up to the most?
- What are your best qualities?
- What is your happiest memory?
- What changes have you implemented into your life for the better?
- If you had one day left on Earth, what would you do?
- Who has impacted your life the most?
- Which film/book do you resonate with the most?
- Which people bring the most joy too your life?
- How have you changed in the past few years?
- What do you feel you need more of in life?
- When do you feel most like yourself?

This page will remain mostly blank on the off chance that you take up peaceful colouring as a hobby, only to realise your pens bleed through the page. If that is the case, here is your prompt to invest in some nice colouring pencils. Treat yourself: get a doughnut while you're at it – you deserve it.

"Draw a monster. Why is it a monster?"
-**Daughter** by **Janice Lee**

Yin & Yang

The concept of yin and yang is said to have originated somewhere around **1300 BC** in **China** and is now recognized as a philosophical principal **internationally**. It works on the basis that all components of life are **opposites** that present as **inseparable** forces that are **complementary** of each other.
For example: light & dark, night & day etc.

Answer the following questions to find out which of the two you are most compatible with.

Are you a **yin** or are you a **yang**?

I prefer the weather in:
   A- winter
   B- summer

I trust in:
   A- my gut
   B- the facts

I am more:
   A- introverted
   B- extroverted

I am more likely to:
   A- oversleep
   B- not sleep at all

I like to eat:
   A- mild foods, dairy and white meats
   B- things packed with flavour and spice

You would find me:
   A- reading a book or in a relaxing bath
   B- going out on the town or doing sports

In the workplace I am:
   A- lazy or procrastinating
   B- proactive and efficient

Mostly A: you align with Yin and its associated traits. People with a Yin personality type tend to be calm introverts who value stability. Often, they are said to have a passive outlook on life and enjoy solitude. Things associated with Yin: cold, nighttime, circles, gentleness, the heart, the right brain, spirituality, slow, still, the moon.

Mostly B: individuals who mainly selected 'B' are considered to have a Yang personality which consists of being a carefree and restless extrovert who seeks out action and brightness. They value order and solidarity. Things associated with Yang: hot, daytime, lines, assertiveness, the mind, the left brain, science, fast, active, the sun.

Deserving

never deny yourself the chance to do
something because you feel you don't
deserve it. You are deserving. You are
worthy.

I shall eat your soul

Autocorrect is undoubtedly genius, a genuinely useful tool (especially to an author like me who is unable to spell <u>bannanna</u> correctly) until you are telling your mum, post-lunchtime:

> i ate your soul, it was out of date

Loneliness

To be lonely is among one of the most
devastating things a human can experience.
To master the art of being alone but never
lonely is nothing but a triumph.
Solitude is bliss.

Deodorant, orange juice and the postman

A good day turned bad can nearly always be salvaged.
A bad day that started bad and stays consistently bad is exceedingly difficult to salvage.
Upon waking we can easily let a niggling 'bad' feeling take us over, tempting us to write the day off as a 'bad day', for it is much easier to let that niggling feeling grow than to try and mute it, especially if our energy reserve is falling short already.
If you can find the strength within you to fight, fight for your right to a good day or at least a good start to the day.

Take care of yourself: brush your teeth, your hair, whip out the deodorant, and your favourite flannel to wash your face, pour yourself a fresh orange juice and enjoy it in the sun, stroke your dog, wave at the postman, read a poem, write a poem and if none of these appeal, at the very least, eat a good breakfast.
Set yourself up for the day.
Start on a serotonin high.

Cherish those who remember small details about you.

'Boredom' remedies

I would always argue that boredom is just a concept imagined up by those with a small imagination.

It is hard to hit boredom if you have a wild imagination or even an imagination of any sort as your brain is a constant provider of activity. However, should you ever achieve a state of perceived boredom, become a people watcher, not only a people watcher but an *advanced* people watcher. Note that there is a very distinct line between advanced people watching and outright stalking.

By my definition, advanced people watching is not just the act of observing passers by going about their daily business or chuckling at a man who thinks no one witnessed him tripping over thin air, advanced people watching is the act of psychoanalysing the people you see or in this case assorting them into different categories.

Step 1 grab a coffee and head to your nearest public area – a bustling high street or a peaceful country park, take your pick.

Step 2 pick one of the following categories to sort the general population into:
Mustard lovers/mustard haters,
Those who prefer red roses vs white roses vs yellow roses,

Monday-Sunday birthdays,
Blur lovers/Oasis lovers,
Zodiac signs,
The list goes on...

[The whole population of the world is
divisible by a great many things, so think of
your own categories if your imagination can
stretch that far and decide, based on a
person's walk, clothing, posture, hairstyle
etc. which category they fall into.]

The unspoken key to success

Your love for: your outlook on life, your actions, your smile, your quirks, your body, your mind, your life, **yourself,** must be greater than your desire to be loved or your efforts to seek external validation.

"Never have I been a calm blue sea, I have always been a storm".
– **Fleetwood Mac**

SECTION TWO

Nonsensical ramblings of a sedated, ADHD-riddled, insomniac

A section dedicated to the absolute bullshit that trickles out of my brain onto paper. Maybe you have regarded this whole book as nonsensical bullshit or maybe you are wandering why I am choosing to include such bullshit in my book.

I choose to publish these slightly delusional ramblings because these are the thoughts that came to me in the dead of night while alarms rang and various sleeping medications and sedatives infiltrated my system in a cold, cold hospital. So even if you read them and – much like me the morning after writing – are struck with confusion at the word heaps I have created, there is always scope for some part of the ramblings to resonate with you in some way. So, take what you can, if anything, from these passages, derive your own meanings from each one. Or alternatively ignore these pages completely.

Lions & lionesses

The lion or lioness inside of you will prevail only in the most desperate moments of your life. Don't fool yourself into believing that you are devoid of courage, if you (fortunately) have not yet experienced utter, all-consuming despair, the beast that bears courage has not yet felt the need to emerge. The emergence of the lion *will* take place and from that moment on the lion will be ever-present, constantly trying to diminish any feelings of despondency.

So, if you *have* had the misfortune of experiencing utter, all-consuming despair, your internal lion is by your side, baring its dagger-like teeth at any of the anguish life hurls at you. Courage prevails when your life depends on it.

Crack it if you can

Sioy mafp xeha ef qip masiqg sio. Yafpiya
sioy huepk uqg **pkyena.**

E kida pkef ahhebeaqpxs bkuxxaqjag sioy
tiqayhox myueq.

Your horses and men

If *ALL* of the King's horses and *ALL* of his men cannot put you back together again, the only person you can truly trust to piece you back together is yourself, potentially with the assistance of all your horses and all your men. But you are the only one who can begin to fix yourself and orchestrate the fixing.

Ock soddities

There is a shop that enables you to buy three socks, a triplet of socks, a triad of socks if you will; no *pair* of socks is to be found in this shop. Each sock is an odd sock that, by rights, should be part of a pair of socks. I think that is a beautiful concept... I am never entirely sure why I consider it *beautiful*, but I do, and you should too.
Sock oddities

Authentic beauty

To be truly beautiful, authentically beautiful,
breathtakingly beautiful is to have both a
beautifully unique mind and a uniquely
beautiful soul.
For beautiful eyes are worthless if no beauty
is to be found in the actions and words and
the soul of the owner of said eyes.

Train ride shenanigans

When you find yourself on a laboriously long train ride with nothing to occupy you other than the endless listing of upcoming stops, conjure up a list of indie-sounding band names and their biggest hits...

Bitten Linen by
The Triumphant Panda Carcasses

Broken Sangria by
The Portfolios.

Little Atom Boy by
Jax and the twenty milkmen.

Sandpaper Unravelling by
Antarctic narcissism.

Hopeful Trampolining by
The 43 predecessors.

Train Ride Shenanigans by
The unconventional minds.

...just don't miss your stop.

Be young

Be young at heart, grab onto youth and don't let go, be happy in the way that a naïve six-year-old who is yet to experience life's hardships is.

Look forward to Christmas, lick the bowl when you've finished baking cookies, go on that rope swing, roll your Easter eggs down a hill and dance carelessly in the rain.

Simplicity

When life feels overwhelmingly complicated, remember you can make a cake with four simple ingredients:

Butter
Sugar
Egg
Flour

Life can be simple, so next time everything feels too much, or like there is a ridiculous number of ingredients needed to create your success, think back to cake and remember:

110g butter
110g sugar
2 eggs
110g flour

Shoutouts

Some recognition for the small, very random, very specific, portion of the general public.

a shoutout to:

- Those who wear raincoats year-round.

- Those called Angela who are reading this on their birthday.

- Those who play Othello every Sunday without fail.

- Those who have a grandad called Tony, who used to own an ice cream van.

- Those who are currently indulging in their strange concoction of cravings.

- Those who are ready to regift this book to a friend who owns a Springer Spaniel.

- Those who have a jaw that clicks every time they eat.

- Those with the surname 'Quinn'.

- Those who visited Peru at the age of 23.

- Those who ignore their lactose intolerance.

- Those who always have lingonberry juice in the fridge.

- Those who had to cancel their tickets for a West End show because they had no one to go with.

- Those who dyed their beard blue within the last 65 hours.

- Those who have a twin sister called Mathilda whose favourite colour is green.

- Those who don't know their eight times tables.

- Those who have Downton Abbey playing as background noise as they read this.

- Those who own yellow socks exclusively.

- Those who have a tattoo of a caterpillar.

- Those born on the 18th of October.

- Those who can devour a full trifle in under a minute.

- Those who have a family in which everyone's name begins with an S.

- Those who reuse their bag for life bags.

- And a special shoutout to those who have bothered to buy and potentially read and hopefully enjoyed this book.

"The day you sort your head out, you are going to contribute. You will be of great use to the world."

– words from the mouth of one of many articulate, brilliant-minded health care professionals who have helped me along the way. (This one, in particular, named Kevin.)

These were the words that pushed me to '*sort my head out*' and make the steps to contribute to the world, my first port of call in doing so being getting this book finished.

Everyone needs a Kevin to spout out nuggets of wisdom when you most need them.

A page of thank yous

If I were to mention every **incredible** healthcare professional who has helped me over the years by name, this solitary page would extend to a long 10 pages, so I'll keep it as short as possible...

A massive thank you to Jess and Pam, the nutritionists who I loved and hated (predominantly loved).

Another massive thanks to Beth and Kelly who made me feel as safe as it is possible to feel as a 17-year-old on a scaryish ward filled with dementia patients who had a tendency to roll onto my bed.

Beth's dog, who visited me on my first admission, also deserves a special mention alongside Ash, Ash 2.0 and Steph.

Jane, who kept me distracted and giggling throughout the night shift and introduced me to the film 'Girl's Trip'. Thanks to Raegan, Charlotte, and Sophie for keeping me smiling through all the tears on my hardest admission to hospital.

Natasha and Ellie, who had the role of dealing with my meltdowns throughout the day more than they should've done.

Mia and Jacqui, who very effectively did the exact same job, throughout the nights whilst dishing out meds, or in Jaqui's case, eagerly encouraging me to write this book.

Thanks to Kevin for consistently reassuring me that I do in fact exist and that the government isn't plotting against me.

And thank you so very much to Vicky for constantly fighting my corner, all whilst making sure I'm still living and breathing; thank you for all your concern regarding my potassium levels.

Thank you for keeping me sane and sincerest apologies for causing many less than adequate nights of sleep.

To all the professionals who saved me and gave me some sense of hope in life, thank you.

The aim of this book is for it to carry the same comfort as the staple Shepherd's Pie your Grandma used to make with love, warmth, compassion and mince. Of course, if your Grandma's attempts at cooking were nothing short of a death sentence or you happen to be a vegan, this analogy does not apply to you.

At the core of this book is a hug when no willing hugger is around or a shoulder to cry on, when all shoulders are occupied. Pages of reassurance that say 'yeah don't worry, I've been there too'.

To some, just a retreat from all the uncertainty and turbulence that life holds...
uncertainty and turbulence that your mildly unconventional brain holds.

Or just a provider of entertainment, unaccompanied by the commitment that a regular storybook or biography requires.

Not dissimilar to a beloved teddy missing an eye and the majority of its stuffing or an expensive but ugly looking heirloom of a necklace, this book can be passed down through generations. Complete with your own annotations, doodles, cuttings and stickings, coffee stains, wine stains, tear stains and a sliver of your soul.

An assembly of hopeful anecdotes, reflections on life, nonsensical utterances, short stories, uplifting reminders that feel so deeply personal yet universally touching. Interspersed between the philosophical thinking and thought-provoking advice pages are pockets of humour, recipes, chinchilla care tips, word-searches...

...a **melange** of enjoyable, bite-sized literature.

Printed in Great Britain
by Amazon